ABOVE AND FRONT COVER: *Blacksmith Roger Mildred at work at his forge in Mentmore, Buckinghamshire.*
OPPOSITE: *'The Smith', an illustration from 'The Book of English Trades'.*

THE VILLAGE BLACKSMITH

Jocelyn Bailey

Shire Publications Ltd

CONTENTS

Printed in Great Britain by C. I. Thomas & Sons (Haverfordwest) Ltd, Press Buildings, Merlins Bridge, Haverfordwest.

ACKNOWLEDGEMENTS
The author is pleased to acknowledge the invaluable help given by the following towards the compiling of this book: The Clerk of the Worshipful Company of Farriers; the curators and staff of the Museum of English Rural Life, University of Reading; University of London, Wye College Agricultural Museum, Brook, near Ashford, Kent; Maidstone Museum; Council for Small Industries in Rural Areas; Kingsnorth Trailer Company; Elizabeth Essex, Sadie Ward, Carrie Sampson, Caroline Rippier; Messrs J. Charman, J. Ferridge, R. Filmer, W. Goldup, E. Leithes, R. Mildred, R. Moseley, J. Rootes, B. Skues, J. Skues, C. Smith, F. Smith, I. Smith, G. Stagg, E. Stern.
Illustrations are acknowledged as follows: Michael Bass, front cover, pages 1, 28 and 29; CoSIRA, pages 13 and 31 (centre and bottom); Richard Filmer, pages 10 (bottom two) and 11; Berham Kapadia, page 7; The Manx Museum, page 5; Museum of English Rural Life, Reading University, inside front cover, pages 2, 3, 4, 8 (top), 10 (top three), 17, 19, 23 (top), 30 (top). The remaining illustrations are from the author's collection.

An illustration of a farrier's workshop, published by William Darton in the early nineteenth century.

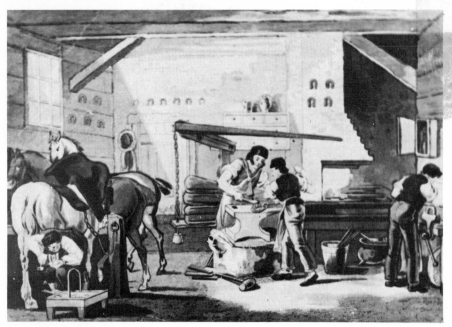

A blacksmith at Bradfield in Berkshire; the date of the photograph is not known.

INTRODUCTION

The English rural tradition of the presence of several specialised hand craftsmen practising in every village has virtually come to an end during the transport and industrial changes of the present century. These individual skills included those of the blacksmith, the wheelwright, the carpenter, the saddler and the harness maker, all of which were based upon the horse as the main means of power and transport. These crafts were needed in most rural places; many other crafts would be found where certain materials were plentiful or where there was local need for skills such as hurdle making, basket making and thatching. Many village craftsmen were of a family tradition, the skills passing from father to son.

The blacksmith's part in the daily needs of village life was vital. He was highly skilled in farriery and he made and repaired tools and equipment for local farms and households.

As the need for village blacksmiths lessened during this century, some of them adapted to kindred occupations such as motor and agricultural engineering or ornamental ironwork, whilst others advised their sons to follow another career altogether. However, smithing and farriery are traditional crafts and a few families and individuals have brought them safely into the 1970s. Apprenticeship to both crafts is now regaining considerable interest and support. They cannot now survive solely as village occupations; today's practical smith or blacksmith forges individual items for a wider clientele, and whereas in former times the local people could take their horses to the nearby smithy, today the farrier or shoeing smith normally travels around to stables over a fairly wide area. Cold shoeing is the usual method now as the equipment for hot shoeing is cumbersome to transport, and even the portable forge fire is not suited to the continual extinguishing and

3

This early photograph of a farriery shows the chestnut trees so often associated with village smithies.

relighting needed for the many calls a busy farrier would expect to fit into a day.

The village craftsmen of former times worked hard and long hours—6 a.m. to 6 p.m. being quite usual. There was no set retirement age, and money was not usually plentiful enough for them to retire on their own account, so they tended to remain at their work until they were quite elderly.

The rural economy of former years had a pattern of its own. Even up until the early part of this century settlement of bills to local tradesmen and craftsmen was done on an annual basis by some customers, and sometimes by barter: the baker might supply bread to the smith in exchange for farriery. People unable to meet their bills with cash might offer something else instead. One old craftsman recalled having received a cow and, on another occasion, a motorcycle combination in this way. The prices charged by craftsmen were consistent between villages, and there was some concern if the price was higher in one village than the next.

In addition to teaching his sons his craft, a craftsman would sometimes take on an occasional apprentice, who would start by paying the master a small weekly fee, then gradually change to receiving a small sum himself as he became more useful at the work.

The old-time forge would usually be sited in the centre of the village it served, quite often near a crossroads. A fairly large forecourt was useful for the waiting horses and vehicles, with a drinking trough and with loops on the walls for tethering the animals. Somewhere outside there would be an iron wheelplate, about six feet in diameter, embedded in the ground for use when a wooden wheel was to be shod with its iron tyre. The chestnut tree, poetically symbolic of the village smithy, would be grown for the shade it cast on hot sunny days.

The reconstructed smithy at the Open Air Folk Museum, Cregneash, Isle of Man.

THE EQUIPMENT AND TOOLS

Inside, the hearth and fire form the forge proper, although now the word 'forge' usually refers to the whole of the smith's working premises. The fire is on a raised hearth, usually of bricks, with a canopy and chimney over it. Some places might have a double hearth, with the bellows system between, serving either hearth as required. The bellows create the draught of air needed to bring the fire to sufficient temperature to heat the iron for working. A lever with a cowhorn handle was used to hand-operate the bellows. (Today an electrically driven blower is often used.) A blast pipe or tuyere projects directly into the fire. It is connected to the bellows by a pipe and is often water-cooled, the water being contained in an open-topped tank behind the hearth. Water is also kept in the cooling trough at the front of the hearth. This is used for cooling tools and for quenching certain work.

Fuel for the fire is supplied by the local coal merchant and consists of the most suitable coals and cokes obtainable in the area. It is a nuisance to work with a fuel which clinkers easily, but the smith keeps the fire at a good working condition by adept use of the fire irons, such as the slice, rake and poker. To assist the work of tending the fire and testing the colour glow of the heated iron, the fire is away from the direct light of a window.

An anvil is, ideally, made of wrought iron, with a steel face added to part of the working surface. At one end of the face is a square hole (called a hardie hole) to hold the shank of a bottom tool. Close to this is a round hole over which small holes can be punched. (Normally, this is used to make the nail holes in horseshoes.) The small part of the work surface not covered with steel is called the table, and this softer area is used for some jobs to prevent

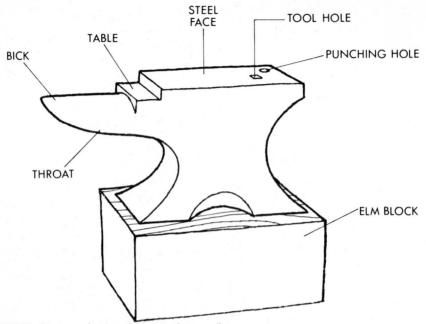

BICK

TABLE

STEEL FACE

TOOL HOLE

PUNCHING HOLE

THROAT

ELM BLOCK

ABOVE: *Diagram showing the parts of an anvil.*
OPPOSITE: *A reconstructed smithy is operated by members of the Pitstone Local History Society during one of its 'open' days at Pitstone, Buckinghamshire.*

damage to hardened tools or to the steel face of the anvil. The pointed end of the anvil is called the bick or beak, with the throat underneath it. The anvil is ideally mounted on a squared-up piece of elm trunk, at a height which suits the individual worker, and usually slopes slightly away from him so that any hot debris falls out of the way.

Another piece of equipment is the mechanical drill, and many varied and interesting examples have existed in older shops. Then there is the large floor mandrel, which helps in the making of various hooped items. The swage block is another distinctive-looking aid, and its many notches, holes and curves help in the shaping of heated iron and the punching of large or irregular holes. Smaller top and bottom swages are also to be found, although some smiths do not consider these to be particularly useful.

The blacksmith has a variety of hammers, each suited to a particular job, and a large sledgehammer that is essential when a striker or hammer-man is assisting

with certain work. Tongs for holding the hot iron are numerous and, like so many of the tools, are often made by the smith or his forebears. There are also drifts and punches for making or enlarging holes.

Tools for cutting iron, both in hot and cold work, consist of chisels, sets and hardies. There are also shears for cutting sheet metal. Fullers are like blunt chisels, and these can consist of single or top and bottom tools.

At the bench is the steel leg vice, typical of every smithy. It often has the leg embedded in concrete in the ground to ensure that both vice and bench will withstand the stresses made on them during various metalwork jobs. Apart from the general processes of forging, cutting, twisting and bending metal, the former smiths often used to make nuts and bolts as required and cut the threads manually with stocks, dies, wrenches and taps. This was laborious and time-consuming work and is not so likely to be done today.

A tyre bender of some kind would be

needed in the village smithy. Some were fairly complex, consisting of several sets of iron rollers, rather like a multiple household wringer, and turned by a handle in much the same way. Other benders were simple bench devices. Even today, a smith can find use for an old bender, such as in the making of a hoop on which to mount a set of lamps to make a light fitting.

LEFT: *A swage block.*

BELOW LEFT: *A steel leg vice.*

BELOW RIGHT: *A floor mandrel (left) and two swage blocks.*

The blacksmith wears a leather apron often fringed along the bottom so that he can brush debris from the anvil with his apron edge. A farrier's apron is split vertically down the lower part so that he can grip a horse's hoof between his thighs when shoeing. The modern blacksmith tends to wear industrial boots with steel toe caps.

RIGHT: *This old tyre bender is still used for bending iron bar for hooped items.*

BELOW LEFT: *Pear-shaped bellows in the collection of the Kingsnorth Trailer Company.*

BELOW RIGHT: *Circular bellows on show at the Maidstone Museum in Kent.*

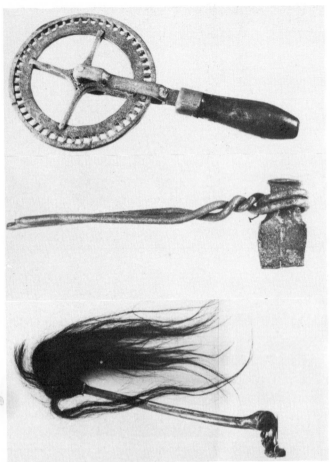

FROM TOP TO BOTTOM: *A traveller for measuring wheels that are to be re-tyred. A hand-held top tool. A farrier's fly switch. Carvings of blacksmith's tools on the choirstalls of the church at St Ives in Cornwall.*

Using a scroll wrench and scroll former to make an ornamental scroll.

MATERIALS AND METHODS

Some retired blacksmiths can still remember the time when wrought iron was their usual material, and the purest wrought iron came from Yorkshire. Mild steel is now the most commonly available material and is just as useful to the smith, although some ways of working it differ slightly. Iron and steel are supplied in lengths of various sections and named, accordingly to trade practice, rounds, hexagons, squares, angles and flats. Light horseshoes are fashioned from fullered bar, and a modern farrier also usually buys a number of machine-made shoes to keep up with the demands of his regular rounds. These need final preparation in his forge with some alterations and the punching of the holes before being suitable for shoeing.

In former times iron would often be used over and over again. Some customers reckoned, too, on having their horses shod with old shoes made into new ones, as it was considered that this method produced a harder-wearing metal. (It needed two old shoes forged together to make one new shoe.) Another method of re-using iron was to cut an old iron wheel tyre into suitable strips and make it into horseshoes. Such methods were time-consuming, but that did not seem to matter so much in those days. Worn out files and rasps were always saved, as they were made of hardened steel and could be refashioned into all kinds of tools and equipment. Many items thus made can be identified by the diamond pattern still showing somewhere.

ABOVE LEFT: *Wall brackets at a village forge carry the various bars and rods of mild steel that the smith uses.* ABOVE RIGHT: *Upsetting or jumping-up a bar in order to shorten and thicken it.*

Metalworking methods in the forge include cutting, forging, bending, fullering, upsetting and fire welding.

Fullering, or drawing down, is done to spread the heated iron to a thinner dimension, thereby lengthening it as well. This is done at the anvil by hammering a fullering tool held against the work. Upsetting, or jumping-up, is almost the opposite, as this is intended to thicken and shorten the metal being worked. It is done by heating the precise part and then applying blows to the end of the whole piece or by 'jumping' the entire piece against the work surface.

Fire welding is another operation in the work of a forge. The key to good welding is in well prepared, clean joint surfaces, a clean, unclinkered fire, and accurate judgement of the colour of the metal when it is at the correct heat. Rapid hammering then produces a successful joint. Silver sand is used to keep the fire and the metal clean. One type of weld is the scarf weld; it is done by tapering and overlapping the ends to be joined. Another is the V weld, in which a V is cut into one piece, and the other piece is let into it. (Acetylene welding is much used today, but forge welding can still hold its own in general usefulness, strength and versatility.)

Fitting wooden wheels with iron tyres was a process which used to be regularly undertaken by the smith. A lot of skill and experience was needed to produce a good result. To fit a tyre to a new wheel, the perimeter of the wooden wheel is first measured with a traveller. The smith makes an allowance for the shrinkage that is needed in the final work and cuts a length of flat iron bar. (This measuring must be correct and an experienced smith checks everything three times before cutting the bar.) The bar is then formed into a circle using a tyre bender and the ends are welded together to make a hoop.

A furnace or a large fire of waste wood or faggots on open ground is needed to heat the hoop for the tyring. Borax is sometimes sprinkled over such a fire to make it burn clearly. The wheel is clamped onto the iron wheelplate set in the ground outside the forge.

When the tyre is sufficiently heated, it is lifted from the fire and lowered over the rim of the wheel. The smith levers the tyre over the rim with iron tyre dogs and helpers follow with sledgehammers to drive the tyre well on to the wheel. When it is evenly fitted, water is poured around the work and amidst the steam the woodwork joints are forced tightly together as the iron shrinks on to the wheel. Apart from new tyres being fitted to new wheels, there were also repaired wheels to be retyred, and sometimes a tyre just needed to be made smaller and refitted. In a busy area the crafts of smith and wheelwright might be combined under one roof.

The tempering of steel by heat is another of the smith's skills and some used to gain a local reputation for themselves by developing methods to produce various cutting tools of high quality and reliability.

Making a rivet for a pair of tongs. On the left, the shank is reduced between top and bottom swages. On the right, the rivet is cut off over a hardie seated in the hardie hole or tool hole of the anvil.

Tyring a wheel.

ABOVE: *Lighting the fire in which there is a set of iron tyres.*

RIGHT: *As the fire burns down, a wooden wheel is clamped on to the iron wheelplate.*

BELOW: *Lowering the red-hot iron tyre on to the wooden wheel rim.*

OPPOSITE TOP: *The tyre is levered over the rim with iron tyre dogs while the tyre is hammered into place.*

OPPOSITE BOTTOM: *After an initial cooling, the tyre is hammered finally into place.*

Cooling the newly tyred wheel in a bath of water. As the hot metal tyre cools it tightens the joints of the wooden wheel.

Farriers, drawn by W. H. Pyne and published in his 'Microcosm' in 1808.

THE FARRIER

Today the work of the farrier or shoeing smith and that of the practical smith or blacksmith are rarely carried out by the same man. They have become separate crafts. But in former times all village blacksmiths wanted to maintain a high reputation for their farriery. It formed the bulk of the work for many. During the nineteenth century the Royal College of Veterinary Surgeons was formed, and in 1881 the first Veterinary Surgeons Act was passed. This relieved the farrier of his additional previous role of horse doctor, and of being expected to diagnose and treat horse ailments. The various instruments a farrier might have had in his possession can be seen in museums. However, he continues to need special knowledge of the anatomy of the horse's limbs, for he makes up corrective and surgical shoes when required.

The horse is a hoofed or ungulate animal. The hoof is continually growing and needs trimming and re-shoeing regularly when a horse is used on hard roads. Those out to grass may not need shoes but still need inspection and trimming.

The shoeing process begins at the anvil as the farrier makes up sets of shoes. (At one time even the nails were made up by hand.) The old shoes are removed from the horse with large pincers. The foot is cleaned and the hoof pared using a searcher, paring knife and rasp. The new shoe is tried and altered as necessary and then nailed on. One of the skills of farriery is ensuring that the nails penetrate only

ABOVE: *Shoeing an ox, about 1880, at Saddlecombe, near Brighton, East Sussex.*
OPPOSITE: *Preparing horseshoes at the forge for a mobile farriery service. This village blacksmith has nearly five hundred years of family connections with the craft.*

the insensitive part of the hoof, for if a nail goes into the sensitive area lameness and other problems occur. The protruding point of each newly applied nail is twisted off with the claw side of the farrier's hammer, and the end is clinched over to hold the shoe on firmly. The hoof is then trimmed with a rasp to finish off. The forefoot can be placed on the farrier's stand for these final touches. Old-timers referred to the farrier's stand as the 'lazy blacksmith' and considered that the farrier should hold the horse's foot in his lap regardless of how tiring this could be.

Shoeing sometimes had problems. Work horses of former years occasionally developed an unpleasant condition called 'greasy leg', the itchiness of which might cause a horse to fidget a lot. Flies were also a nuisance — hence the farrier's fly switch. And during the winter, working horses might have to have frost nails added to their shoes.

Many smiths saw service in the First World War as farriers, and those at home helped to make the many horseshoes required at the front. The eventual demand was so great that machine-made shoes had to be used.

Records of the City of London show that the Guild of Farriers existed in 1356. In 1674 it became the Worshipful Company of Farriers by royal charter granted by Charles II. This gave the company special privileges and the duty of fostering a high standard of farriery within the liberties of London and Westminster and seven miles beyond.

In 1890 the Company inaugurated a registration scheme for shoeing smiths and appointed a Registration Committee to supervise it and hold examinations. In 1958 the Company introduced an apprenticeship scheme, farriery having steadily declined as a career owing to the decrease in the horse population, but a new demand was by now quickly springing up as a result of the surge of interest in

RIGHT: *A master farrier giving a demonstration of hot-shoeing at a village festival.*

FAR RIGHT: *Holding the hot shoe against the hoof gives a guide to any alterations needed to make the shoe a perfect fit.*

riding and driving as leisure pursuits. This scheme was, therefore, of mutual benefit to all concerned — and especially in the ever present need for fostering the standards of farriery to protect the wellbeing of horses.

In June 1979 government legislation came into force requiring that only those fully qualified and registered under the Farriers Registration Act would be allowed to shoe horses. A Main Apprenticeship Scheme has consequently been formed, assisted from public funds and administered by CoSIRA under the jurisdiction of the Farriery Apprenticeship Regulating Committee consisting of delegates from all bodies directly concerned with the training of farriers and a high standard of farriery.

Usual age of entry to apprenticeship is sixteen to nineteen years and it lasts four years. Addresses for enquiries about Farriery Apprenticeship matters are noted inside the back cover of this book and careers advisers may also be consulted.

Hot-shoeing.

ABOVE LEFT: *Nailing on the shoe.*

ABOVE RIGHT: *The end of the new nail being removed with the claw side of the hammer.*

LEFT: *Using the jaw of the pincers as a support, the farrier clinches over the end of a new nail with his hammer.*

TOP: *This old photograph shows a blacksmith doing a 'remove', that is taking off the old shoe with pincers.*

ABOVE: *The tools of the mobile farrier. The piece of iron near the smaller box makes a useful portable anvil.*

THE WORSHIPFUL COMPANY OF FARRIERS

New Armorial Bearings granted
11th September, 1968

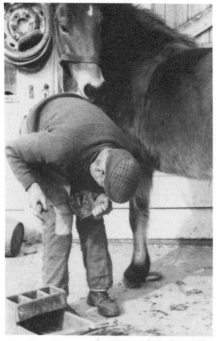

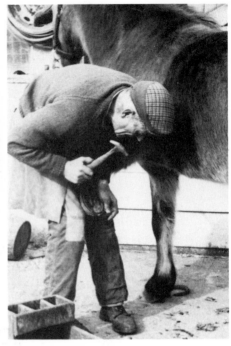

Cold-shoeing.

ABOVE LEFT: *Trimming the hoof ready for shoeing.*

ABOVE RIGHT: *The master farrier starts to nail on the shoe.*

LEFT: *With a quick wrist movement, the farrier removes the end of a new shoe nail protruding through the hoof.*

RIGHT: *More nails fix the shoe firmly to the hoof.*

Cold-shoeing.

ABOVE LEFT: The hoof is placed on the farrier's stand in readiness for clinching and trimming.

ABOVE RIGHT: The apprentice clinches the shoe nails, using the stand, or 'lazy blacksmith', to steady the hoof.

LEFT: The shoeing is finished with a final light rasping of the hoof.

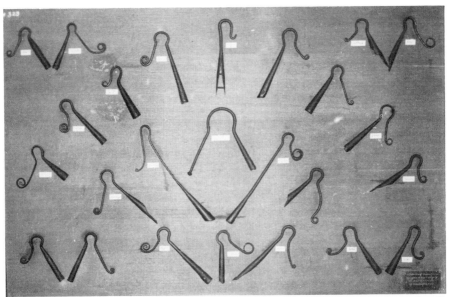

This collection of shepherds' crooks was given to Wye College Agricultural Museum by the Rev. R. W. H. Acworth in 1948. It demonstrates the skilled work of the village smiths who made them.

AGRICULTURAL AND ORNAMENTAL WORK

The village blacksmith used to make and repair innumerable hand tools and pieces of equipment for local farms — hoes, forks, dock lifters, harrows, shepherd's crooks, and the like.

Some of the equipment was made in conjunction with the village carpenter and the wheelwright, like the iron fittings for farm wagons and carts. If a wheelwright ordered a set of irons for a certain size of vehicle, the blacksmith knew exactly what was needed. Wooden harrows made by the carpenter had iron fittings from the forge. (The smith often made harrows completely of iron.)

Sometimes a smith was asked to make an item a customer had designed or invented, often a mechanical idea for agricultural use.

Ornamental work occasionally made a change for the village smith for, although most of his time would of necessity be taken up with the utilitarian objects wanted by his customers, many items gave him an opportunity to combine decoration with utility — screens, garden furniture, gates, fences, weathervanes, door irons and fire irons.

The more humdrum household and garden articles that were made or repaired included candle holders and other lighting aids, cooking utensils, locks, hinges and boot scrapers.

Children would take their broken play hoops along to the smithy for repair. This was a tricky repair, with the smith sometimes ending up with hardly any hoop at all, as the awkward little weld easily overheated and might need several tries. The charge would be a penny. No matter how tiresome and difficult a particular job turned out to be, the charge made was the

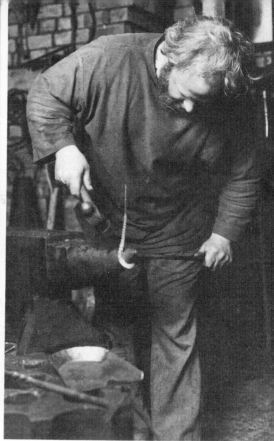

same as though everything had been straightforward. For example, farm horses would sometimes be taken to the smith because the hooves had become overgrown, and yet the shoes might not be at all worn. This meant removing the shoes, trimming the hooves and replacing the same shoes, but often the charge would only be made as for 'removes'.

The blacksmith was a key worker when it came to making tools and appliances for other craftsmen. There is no better tribute to his skills than the motto of the Worshipful Company of Blacksmiths: 'By hammer and hand all arts do stand'.

Roger Mildred, the blacksmith at Mentmore in Buckinghamshire, shows the final stages of completing a twisted rat-tailed handle for one of a set of fire irons. Having forged a long, square taper and twisted it, he bends it at the root before (above left) starting the eye over the beak of the anvil. He then brings the tail over (above), completes the eye (opposite, top left), and wraps the tail around the stem (opposite, top right). The finished handle is shown bottom right.

ABOVE: *An example of ornamental ironwork.*

RIGHT: *A three-pronged hop-garden spud, among the repair jobs at a village forge of today.*

BELOW: *This anvil in stone at Headcorn in Kent marks the grave of a village blacksmith.*

ABOVE: *This 1938 photograph of a new wagon shows some of the iron fittings which a blacksmith would have supplied: (a) shaft staples and harness hooks, (b) shaft irons, (c) iron tyre, (d) shore irons, (e) fittings and chain for roller scotch.*

LEFT: *A trace hook being curved over the beak of the anvil.*

BELOW: *Some finished harness hooks.*